Young Heroes

BADU BOYS RULE!

Dianne Bates
Steven Hallam

RISING★STARS

First published in the UK by
Rising Stars UK Ltd.
7 Hatchers Mews, Bermondsey Street, London SE1 3GS
www.risingstars-uk.com

This edition published 2011

Text © UC Publishing Pty Ltd.
www.ucpublishing.com

First published 2006 by Insight Publications Pty Ltd.
ABN 57 005 102 983,
89 Wellington Street,
St Kilda, Victoria 3182
Australia

Development: UC Publishing Pty Ltd
Cover design: UC Publishing/Design Ed
Written by: Dianne Bates
Illustrations: Steven Hallam
Text design and typesetting: Design Ed/Clive Sutherland
Editorial consultancy: Dee Reid

British Library Cataloguing in Publication Data.
A CIP record for this book is available from the British Library.

ISBN: 978-1-84680-805-0

Printed by Craft Print International Ltd., Singapore

Contents

Characters

Chapter 1
Sunday morning

'A party!' shouts Ina. 'Great! I love parties!'

'What party?' I ask.

'On TI,' she says. TI is Thursday Island. Thursday Island is a few hours away from the island where we live – the island of Badu. Ina loves going to TI. That's where the best guys hang out, she says. Ina loves guys. She's fifteen and silly.

'Church first,' says Dad. He's trying to get us all to hurry. Dad's the vicar. And the vicar is never late.

My little brother Ernie is kicking up a fuss. He hates wearing shoes. So do I. But Dad says we must all wear shoes to church.

Ina poses in front of the mirror. She thinks she's so pretty. Mali and I look around for Ernie's shoes.

We can't find them.

'Hurry!' says Mum.

We look everywhere. Then I find them. Our new puppy has half-chewed one of them. But it's good enough. Off we go.

As we walk, we talk about the party. Think about the big feast to come. Roasted pig. Crayfish. Yams. Mangoes. And lots of cakes. TI women love to bake cakes. And I love to eat them.

'There'll be music,' says Mali. She dances about and claps her hands.

'Mali!' Mum is not pleased. 'No dancing in front of the church!'

Mali stops straight away. 'Sorry,' she says. We stand with Dad and greet our friends at the church door. Everyone knows us—the vicar's family.

I try to be polite and friendly. But all the time I'm thinking of the party. What a great time we'll have!

Chapter 2
The best island in the Cape

Now church is over and we are getting ready to head for the party on TI.

Thursday Island is OK and I like to visit. But I think Badu is a better place. The best island in the Cape. The best in the world.

People come from all over to visit my island. Tourists come in on the ferry. They like Badu too—the ocean, the beaches. And the people. Badu people are the best!

'Bye!' shouts my best mate Wesley. Today he's helping out with the tourists. They like to take lots of pictures. Cameras flash. Everyone wants to remember Badu.

Uncle Joseph is helping Dad with the boat. 'The weather's going to be rough, George,' he says. 'Do you have enough fuel?'

'We'll be fine,' Dad says.

Aunty May gives Mum a basket of food. 'Have a good time, Ruby.' She kisses Mum, Ernie and the girls. She's not going to kiss me! I hate kisses.

At last the boat is ready. Uncle Joseph gives me a high five and we're off. Only a few hours from now and we'll be at TI.

Chapter 3
All at sea

'This doesn't look good,' Dad says. Uncle Joseph was right. There's bad weather. 'Looks as if there might be a storm.'

Lightning zigzags across the sky. Thunder booms. The waves are really big. Ernie is crying. I bet I didn't cry when I was little.

THIS DOESN'T LOOK GOOD.

Our boat rocks up and down in the big waves.

Once I was in my Uncle's boat with a tourist when the waves were big. The tourist's face went green. He leaned over the side and threw up. Seven times he threw up. Badu Islanders never throw up. We're tough. And the toughest are Badu boys. Like me.

'Oh no!' cries Dad.

There's a big bang from the boat's motor. And then it stops as if it's died.

'What is it, George?' Mum asks.

Dad looks worried. He's no mechanic.

'I don't know,' he says.

Now that we've stopped, the waves seem even bigger. They rock our boat up and down, up and down. I've never been in such big waves. Not even when I've been out fishing in Torres Strait.

Ernie is crying really loudly. Mali is screaming.

'Put on the life jackets,' Dad says.

There are only four of them. One for each of us kids.

Suddenly the boat rolls. Right up high. Higher than ever. It rocks to the other side. Water flies up and soaks us.

'God help us!' Mum's face is almost white.

This is our worst nightmare. The boat swings up again. High. Higher. Higher. And then it flips over.

Chapter 4
In deep water

When this day started it was the best day. We were so excited. Setting off for a party on TI.

Now, it is the worst day. We're all in the water. My whole family. I'm up to my neck. Water is in my mouth and up my nose. Mali is screaming. Ina is crying and so is Ernie. Crying so loudly they must hear him back on Badu. Mum and Dad are holding him. He keeps wriggling. Their faces look worried.

Our boat has gone. Slipped under the choppy waves. Down to the bottom of the sea. Down to a watery grave. Is that what will happen to us? We're miles from home. And miles from TI.

I'm the strongest swimmer. I swim over to Mum and Dad.

'What are we going to do?' I yell.

A big wave bobs up. I swallow another mouthful. It fills my lungs with water. I almost choke. Yuk!

'See those rocks over there?' Dad points to the south. They're about half a kilometre away. 'Swim there, son. Take Mali and Ina with you.'

I don't want to leave half my family behind. But I always do what Dad says.

'God will take care of us,' Mum says. 'And he will take care of you children.'

Another wave swamps us all. Water covers Ernie's head. Soon he bobs up, choking and crying. Poor kid. He's only three. And he can't swim. Not like us older kids.

'I love you, Mum, Dad, Ernie,' I call. For a moment I'm glad I'm in the water. Nobody can see my tears. I'm a Badu boy. Badu boys never cry.

I swim around Mum and Dad. Mali and Ina tread water. They're crying—loudly. Mali doesn't want to leave. 'Let me stay with you,' she begs.

'No!' Dad sounds cross. 'We've only one life jacket between us. Your mum and I need to stay with Ernie.'

The waves sweep over Mali. Then she bobs up again. 'Please, Daddy!' she cries.

'Go! Now!' Dad yells.

'Come on!' I call. I want to kiss Mum and Dad. Tell them I love them. But I turn and start swimming.

One arm over the other. Legs kicking. On and on I swim. When I've gone a fair way, I take a rest and turn. I can't see Mum and Dad and Ernie. But I can see Ina and Mali is not far behind her. Then a big wave comes up and they disappear from my sight.

Chapter 5
On the rocks

'We can't stay here forever.' Ina is three years older than me and bossy. She wants us to keep swimming. Matu Island is miles away. It took us ages to get this far. Many hours of swimming. But it will take much, much longer to get to Matu.

We've been on the rocks for a day now. There is nothing to eat. Nothing to drink. Worst of all, we cannot see our mum, dad and little brother. We kept looking back on our long swim. Now and again we saw them. But then we couldn't. We are all worried about them.

Mali has not stopped crying. 'They've drowned!' she keeps saying.

'They're OK,' I tell her. I'm not sure if they are or not. But I want to hope for the best.

The island we're on is not really an island. It's just rocks. Smaller than my bedroom. I can take five steps either way, that's how small it is.

'I'm hungry,' moans Ina. For the hundredth time.

Just then, I see a coconut. It's a fair way off, floating on the water. But the tide might just bring it to us.

'I wish we had a stick,' I say. 'Or a palm leaf.'

I'm so thirsty. It rained during the night. But now the sun is high in the sky. And it's hot. Hotter than it usually is this time of year.

Mali curls into a little ball. She's still sobbing.

Ina and I watch that coconut. It's lonely. It wants us. We want it!

All day we watch the coconut. It inches closer and closer. So slowly! But closer ...

At long last, the tide is kind. The coconut is ours!

I smash it on the rock, trying not to spill the milk.

'Here,' I say to Mali. Anything to stop her crying.

She drinks the coconut milk. Then Ina and I drink until it is all gone.

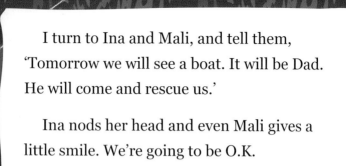

I turn to Ina and Mali, and tell them, 'Tomorrow we will see a boat. It will be Dad. He will come and rescue us.'

Ina nods her head and even Mali gives a little smile. We're going to be O.K.